Angel Kisses

Written by Ginny Kelley
and Katie Kelley Dorn
Illustrated by Amanda Garcia
and Annie Danielson

Published by Nantucket Publications

Acknowledgements

I would like to thank my sister, Katie Kelley Dorn, who helped me put my words into a loving message to my girls. Also to Annie Danielson, and her friend Amanda Garcia, for the beautiful illustrations that capture our life and story. To my lambies, thank you for giving me inspiration to carry on. And finally, I would not have been able to thrive on my journey with breast cancer without my parents, my sisters, and all of my dear friends and Ginnypals who support me each and every day. God Love Ya All!

Ginny Kelley

Printed in the United States.

Library of Congress Cataloging-in-Publication Data

Kelley, Ginny, 1957-
Angel Kisses / Ginny Kelley.
Summary: A heartwarming message of love and comfort from a mother with terminal breast cancer to her three young children.
ISBN 0-9640534-2-1
1. Grief – Fiction 2. Stories that rhyme.

Dedication

To my three little lambies
Rosie, Lily and Josie

Sweet
Dreams

Oh my three little Lovies,

Who Loves you the biggest?

My three little Lambies,

Who loves you the best?

Sweet
Dreams

Every night before bedtime
I say the same rhymes.
Every night you all answer
The same way, the same time.
Mama loves me the biggest.
Mama loves me the best.

We are a great family, the four of us lambs,

We like to dance crazy and read books in our Jams.

You frolic in our garden on our long summer days,

While I dig in my flowers, smiling as you play.

HOME IS WHERE
THE HEART IS
TISSUE

But Mama got sick and my body got weak,

I tried to get better, and doctors did seek.

Medicines, pills, potions and all,

I took them until they made my hair fall.

Mt.
EVEREST

I would have climbed Mt. Everest
If it meant that I could
Stay here with my Lambies
And make my weak body good.

HEAVENLY PLAN
WITH LOVE
he Big Hand

When I didn't get better, I got really mad.

I didn't want to leave you, and I just felt so sad.

So I prayed to God, "Please help me understand,"

And with Love, He showed me His Heavenly Plan.

I finally understood that I'm not leaving at all,

I'm going to Heaven to answer God's call.

You see, God's got a big job for me to do,

I'm going to be an Angel to watch over you.

And like a flower in our garden that blooms every May,

You will continue to blossom even though I'm away.

Cuz I'll always be with you, like the sun in the sky,

I'll shine down and guide you from Heaven on High.

Sweet
Dreams

So when you climb into bed at the end of your day
Close your eyes and remember what I always say,
Who loves you the biggest? Who loves you the best?
Mama loves you the biggest. Mama loves you the best.

BEDTIME STORIES

And then, like always, I'll kiss you goodnight,
But with soft Angel kisses, so tender, so light.
You'll know that they're mine even though we're apart,
Because my spirit lives on inside your heart.

About the Author

Ginny Kelley is the 44-year-old mother of her three adopted daughters, Rosie, Lily and Josie. When faced with the real possibility of her own death from metastasized breast cancer, Ginny wanted to leave her daughters with the strong, comforting image that she would always be in their heart and that God has a heavenly plan for all of us. This book is tucked away in a special place for the girls to receive as comfort at the appropriate time. Until then, Ginny wanted to share the message of love with children who may gain comfort from these reassuring words and illustrations. Ginny currently lives in Edina, MN with her three lambies and fights the battle against breast cancer daily with hope and faith.

To Order This Book from Nantucket Publications:

Visit www.angel-kisses.com to order online or send your order including $11.95/book plus $4.50 for shipping and handling to Angel Kisses, Nantucket Publications, 5524 Nantucket Rd, Minnetonka, MN 55345.